Monsters From

CW00671059

Introduction

Why was the beach wet?
Because the seaweed.

Why did the sailor wear an old dead flatfish?
To ward off the foul demons lurking beneath the waves, of course.

This book covers four salty sea monsters.

The Anything Eel eats anything it touches.
The Giant Sea Slug carves out huge grooves in the sea bed.
Scorpion Prawns suck up seagulls.
The Old Sea Dog lives on and on and on and on.

Published by CGP

Contents

The Anything Eel

An Anything Eel is just a big mouth attached to a little brain and a long tail.

Tiny Brain
The Anything Eel isn't clever enough to pick food from a menu. If it saw a menu it would eat it. Then it would eat the waiter and the restaurant.

Giant Mouth
You can see from the huge teeth that the Anything Eel doesn't eat just salad. It eats anything and everything.

The Sharpest Teeth in the Ocean
These come in handy when the Eel is munching through rock and metal.

Big Eyes
All Anything Eels see is the blur of its own gnashing teeth.

Tail Light
Sea creatures come to look at the pretty light. Then they get shredded, like moths in a lawn mower.

The Anything Eel

Food

It's called an Anything Eel because it eats anything.

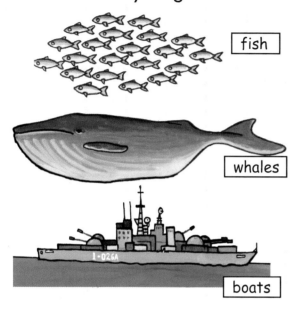

fish

whales

boats

its own tail

Enemies

If it spots its own tail it eats as much of itself as it can.

Sometimes an Anything Eel spots its own tail...

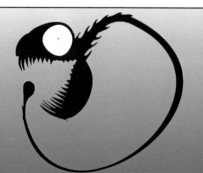

...and decides to have a little taste...

...and munches itself into little bits.

The Anything Eel

Catching Food

ome animals have clever ways of catching food...

...the Anything Eel doesn't.

The Anything Eel has a very simple way of catching food. It takes three steps:

STEP 1

It opens and shuts its mouth really quickly.

STEP 2

It swims around like a turbo-charged fish blender.

STEP 3

It never stops.

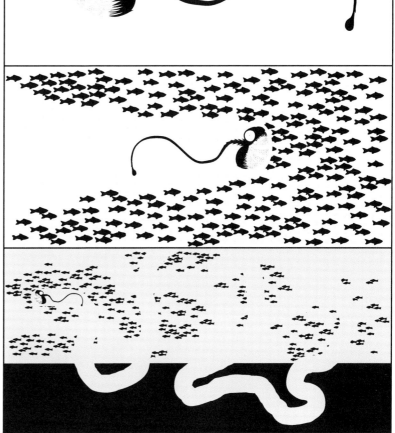

The Anything Eel

Life Cycle

The only time an Anything Eel isn't eating is when it's inside an egg.

- Most fish hide their eggs so they won't get eaten.

- The Anything Eel lays a bright, glowing egg out in the open.

- All the horrible things that live at the bottom of the sea come close to eat it.

- The cute baby Anything Eel hatches. Then it eats holes through all the scary sea creatures. Lovely.

- Anything Eels spend the rest of their lives eating, until the day they eat themselves.

The Anything Eel

How to Spot One

To spot an Anything Eel, just follow the trail of Anything Eel-sized holes.

Anything Eels are always moving and always eating.
Look out for the tell-tale holes like the ones below.

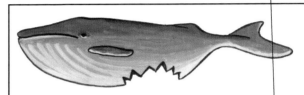

To get a picture of an Anything Eel, you need three things:

- a high-speed camera

- a quick exit

- very little sense

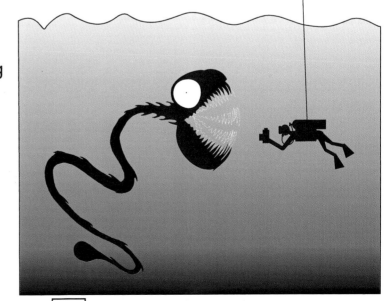

The Giant Sea Slug

The Giant Sea Slug

The Giant Sea Slug is a massive, rock-eating slug at the bottom of the sea.

Unbreakable Scales
Even an Anything Eel would break its teeth on these.

One Massive Eye
It watches out for its only enemy — the Moon Crow.

No Nose
So how does it smell? Terrible.
The smell of a Giant Sea Slug can kill.

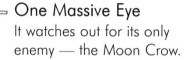

Giant Sea Slug: outer surface

Hard Teeth
These are tough enough to munch through the seabed.

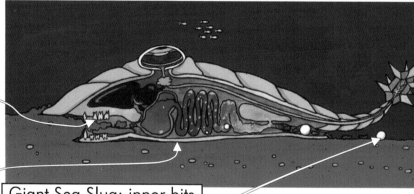

Giant Sea Slug: inner bits

Soft Belly
This is what Moon Crows aim for when they attack.

Pearl Plops
Lumps of rock get stuck in the Sea Slug's belly. T
rocks get covered in layers of grot. The grot buil
up and is smoothed by the guts into giant pearls.

The Giant Sea Slug

Food

Giant Sea Slug has a varied diet. It eats mud, rock, sand and sea life.

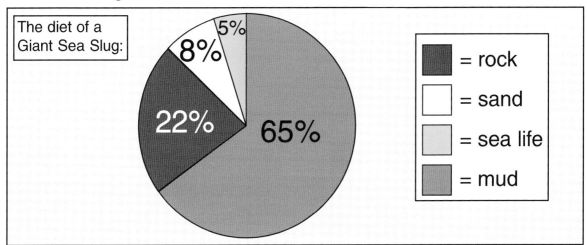

The diet of a Giant Sea Slug:

5%
8%
22%
65%

= rock
= sand
= sea life
= mud

Enemies

Giant Sea Slugs never know when a Moon Crow might attack.

Moon Crows can sniff out the Giant Sea Slug from high in the sky.

When a Moon Crow smells the stink of a Giant Sea Slug, it dives through rock to attack it from underneath.

Find out more about the Moon Crow in the "Monsters From the Sky" book.

The Giant Sea Slug

Catching Food

It moves a bit, it eats the floor. It moves a bit more, it eats some more floor

Catching rock isn't tricky, but chewing it needs some pretty tough teeth.
This article, in "Tooth Times", is about the teeth of the Giant Sea Slug.

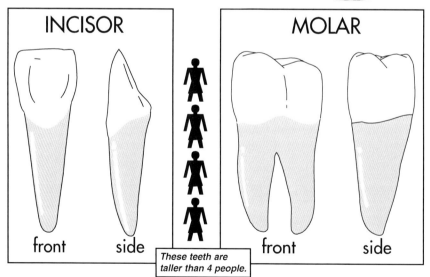

The Monstrous Molars of the Giant Sea Slug

Deep-sea dentist Dr. Pullem returned yesterday from the sea floor.
He had just made the dental discovery of the decade.

Dr. Pullem has winched two giant teeth from the inky depths. They
are a molar and an incisor from the monstrous Giant Sea Slug.

The sharp incisors chomp into the rocky seabed.
The flat-ended molars grind the rock into pieces
before it can be swallowed and digested.

Report by Floss Avery-Day

INCISOR

front   side

MOLAR

front   side

These teeth are
taller than 4 people.

Tooth Times, No. 456   23

The Giant Sea Slug

Life Cycle

Giant Sea Slugs grow up in bubbles of gas. Very smelly gas.

A Baby Giant Sea Slug is born in a bubble of gas. It flies around in the bubble with tiny wings.

The gas bubble stinks. As the bubble rises it kills everything it touches.

The bubble bursts on the surface. The baby flies out. Its wings drop off and it plops back into the sea.

As it sinks to the bottom, the baby eats everything that was killed by the horrible, stinky bubbles.

The Giant Sea Slug spends the rest of its days gobbling up the seabed...

...until the day when the Moon Crow comes for dinner.

 # The Giant Sea Slug

How to Spot One

You can either look out for the flying Sea Slug babies or go deep underwate

- Sailors keep an eye out for stinky gas bubbles and flying baby Sea Slugs.
- If a sailor spots a bubble, they sail away as quickly as possible before the stink destroys the boat.

- Giant Sea Slugs leave behind enormous pearls.
- Greedy divers try to take the pearls, but each pearl is guarded by a Pearl Shark.

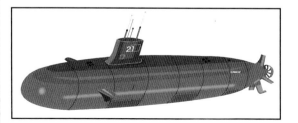

- Submarines can find Giant Sea Slugs using sonar.
- Sonar makes a "ping" sound that bounce off things to give a picture of them.

Scorpion Prawns

Scorpion Prawns look like massive, colourful prawns with nasty tails.

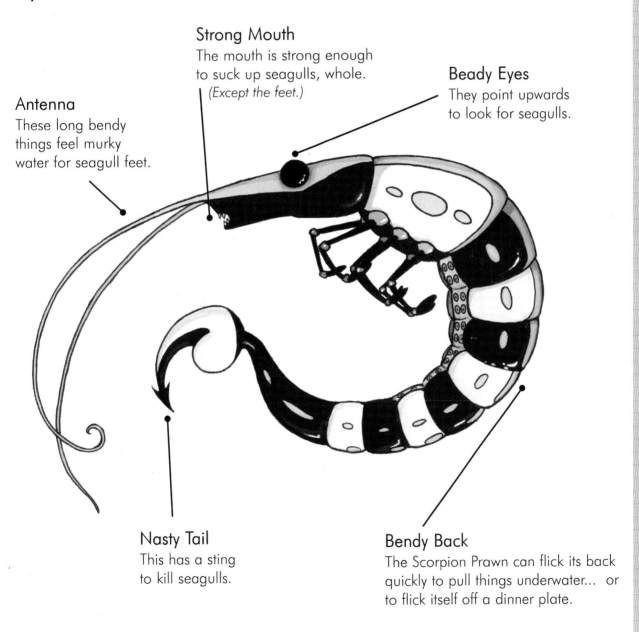

Strong Mouth
The mouth is strong enough to suck up seagulls, whole.
(Except the feet.)

Beady Eyes
They point upwards to look for seagulls.

Antenna
These long bendy things feel murky water for seagull feet.

Nasty Tail
This has a sting to kill seagulls.

Bendy Back
The Scorpion Prawn can flick its back quickly to pull things underwater... or to flick itself off a dinner plate.

Scorpion Prawns

Food

Scorpion Prawns eat seagulls, but they'll try other things if they get peckish

Seagull

other things

Enemies

Scorpion Prawns sometimes get caught in the nets of bearded fishermen.

Some wicked fishermen paint the Scorpion Prawns pink and sell them as giant tasty prawns.

Scorpion Prawns don't make a good meal.

They tend to jump off the plate and attack you.

Catching Food

corpion Prawns catch food quickly. Seagulls are often caught in mid-squawk.

1. The Scorpion Prawn swims closely underneath a seagull.

2. With a flick of its tail, the seagull is pulled underwater.

3. The seagull is sucked up in a blur of feathers and beak.

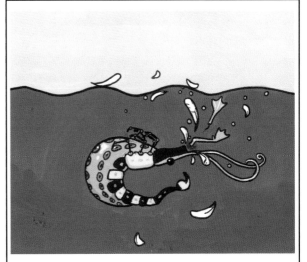

4. The feet are left for baby Scorpion Prawns to chew.

Scorpion Prawns

Life Cycle

A Scorpion Prawn carries eggs on its belly. The eggs look like baked beans

A Scorpion Prawn lays about one hundred eggs. It sticks the eggs to its belly with its legs.

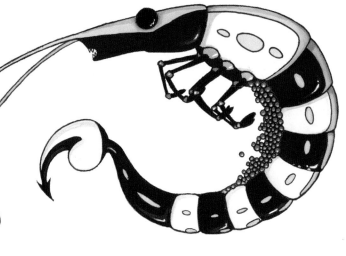

Baby Scorpion Prawns hatch when they are about three centimetres long.

After hatching, the babies stay close to the mother for safety.

The babies eat the leftover bits of seagull.

After a year each baby will start catching its own seagulls.

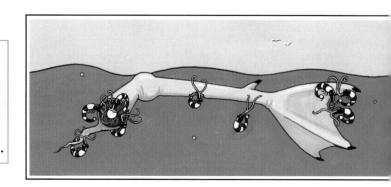

Scorpion Prawns

How to Spot One

potting a Scorpion Prawn in your lunch could save your life (or your fork).

Sometimes Scorpion Prawns are caught and served up as scampi. This is a problem because being fried annoys them and being boiled tickles them.

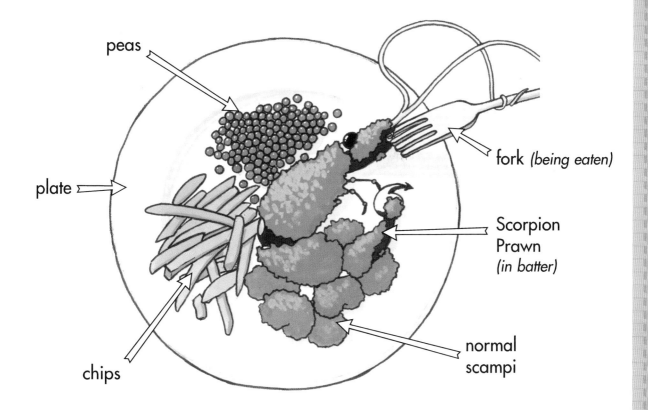

peas

fork *(being eaten)*

plate

Scorpion Prawn *(in batter)*

chips

normal scampi

General rule of thumb:

If your scampi bites your thumb, DON'T EAT IT — RUN.

The Old Sea Dog

The Old Sea Dog is big, fat, old and slow, but it lives for a thousand years.

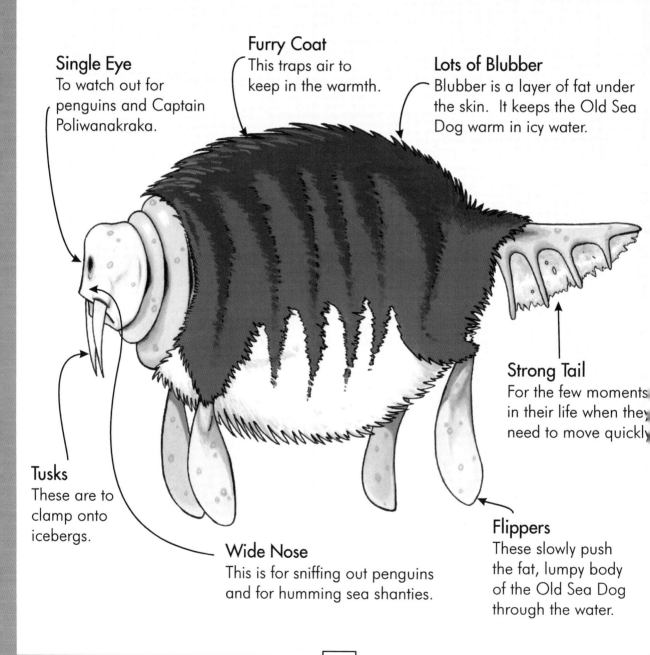

Single Eye
To watch out for penguins and Captain Poliwanakraka.

Furry Coat
This traps air to keep in the warmth.

Lots of Blubber
Blubber is a layer of fat under the skin. It keeps the Old Sea Dog warm in icy water.

Strong Tail
For the few moments in their life when they need to move quickly.

Tusks
These are to clamp onto icebergs.

Wide Nose
This is for sniffing out penguins and for humming sea shanties.

Flippers
These slowly push the fat, lumpy body of the Old Sea Dog through the water.

Food

Old Sea Dogs slurp penguins off icebergs like peas off a plate.

There are lots of different types of penguin. The Old Sea Dog eats them all.

Enemies

One Old Sea Dog is hunted by Captain Poliwanakraka.

Twenty years ago an Old Sea Dog called Barnac ate the boat and the leg of a pirate called Captain Poliwanakraka.

The Captain had his leg replaced with a harpoon. He swears to spend the rest of his days hunting the beast that took his boat.

The Old Sea Dog

Catching Food

Old Sea Dogs love the taste of chilled penguins with warm, gooey centres.

- The Old Sea Dog sniffs out a group of penguins.

- It swims underwater in a big circle to pick up speed.

- It launches out of the water on to the ice.

- It plants its tusks into the ice and opens wide.

- All the penguins slide down the ice into its mouth. Mmm... penguins.

The Old Sea Dog

Life Cycle

The early years of an Old Sea Dog are like penguin Pacman*.   (*See glossary.)

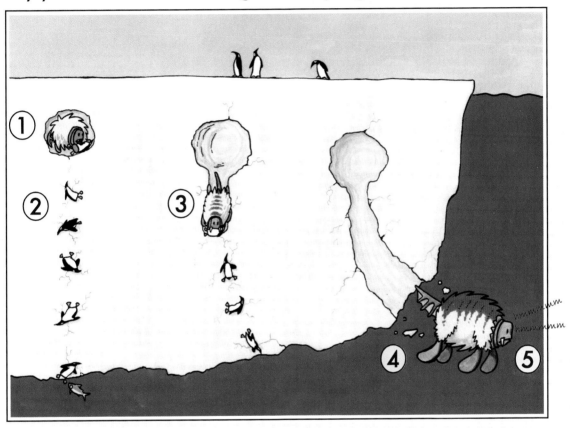

1. The baby Old Sea Dog is born in a deep ice cave. The ice protects it.

2. The parents leave a trail of penguins through the ice to the sea.

3. The baby digs down through the ice from penguin to penguin.

4. When it reaches the sea it is big enough and ugly enough to look after itself.

5. It will spend the rest of its life eating penguins and humming.

The Old Sea Dog

How to Spot One

This is a page from "The tale of Barnac and the Pirate" by Captain Poly.

The wind was doing its best to shred me sails and the ice was trying to rip apart me hull. But I held firm to the mast.

Then across the freezing, foggy waters I heard her. 'Twas the low rumbling hum of Barnac, alright. 'Twas Barnac, the Dog that took me leg, me crew and me sanity.

I'd been following the trail of pengee bodies and Barnac's eerie low humming for the best part o' twenty years.

I leapt out onto the ice and skidded to a stop amongst the little pengees.
As Barnac rose to take the berg, I hurled myself at her, with my harpoon leg aimed at her single eye...

Captain Poly uses odd words. This is what he means:
He uses "*me*" when he means "my".
'Twas = it was
o' = of
pengee = penguin
berg = iceberg